A Twist of Lemon | Lemon Tree Writers

*Prose & Poetry by*
*Lemon Tree Writers*

# A Twist
# of Lemon

**EDITORIAL TEAM**
Cat Brown (prose and poetry)
Eddie Gibbons (poetry)
Aidan Mulkerrin (prose)
Knotbrook Taylor (poetry)

Brenda Conn (editorial assistant)
Martin Walsh (editorial assistant)

*Lemon Tree Writers thank all members of the editorial team for their time and dedication in helping to bring 'A Twist of Lemon' to publication.*

\* \* \*

Published by Lemon Tree Writers in 2021
Copyright remains with the respective authors

Book design by Lumphanan Press
www.lumphananpress.co.uk

Printed & bound by ImprintDigital.com, UK

ISBN: 978-0-9930319-3-9

# Contents

## Editorial | Eddie Gibbons

IN 1995, WHEN I WROTE the editorial for 'Left to Write', the first anthology of work by the Lemon Tree Writers, little did I think I'd be doing the same 26 years later. Thankfully, I remain good friends with Todd McEwen, from whose Writer in Residence workshops the LTW emerged. And I still have the photocopied text of a prose piece entitled 'Tuesday Lunch', which was handed to me by a new group member back in the early days. I thought it was a very good story. I wasn't wrong. Her name was Leila Aboulela.

In the mid-1990s, John Smith of Aberdeen City Council was our greatest promoter, providing us with opportunities to share a stage with the likes of Edwin Morgan, Don Paterson, Alison Flett and many more. Shona Powell, the Lemon Tree director, provided funding to invite Les Murray and Brian Patten to read in the venue.

I later invited Roddy Lumsden, another Aberdeen Writer in Residence, to chair a few group meetings before he moved on to fame, if not fortune, in London. RIP Roddy – gone far too soon.

The fact that the group is still thriving is glowing testimony to everyone who has been actively involved in its development and promotion in the intervening years. Since the early days of LTW at the Lemon Tree in 1993, the group has met in various locations around the city – the Douglas Hotel, Torry community centre, the Belmont Filmhouse. Since March 2020, and for the duration of pandemic restrictions, meetings continue online with members long-standing and new.

The writing in this anthology is testament to the nurturing nature of the group, which provides support and encouragement to new and experienced writers in an environment where their talents can flourish.

*Eddie Gibbons*
*Inaugural Chair of Lemon Tree Writers*

## Imbolc | Sarah-Jane Toleman

St Brigid's day; the beginning of Spring.
Tight buds burgeon.
Ewes carry their lambs,
waiting.

I watch the evening sky
for signs of day's lengthening
as starlings swirl their patterns
in the twilight
and wind's new broom
whisks away last year's leaves.

Sweep out the house.
Gather new rushes.
Prepare the hearth and light candles.
Lay out the feast
and welcome St Brigid,
the sun in her hair.

Then badger wakes from his slumber,
as the Cailleach
prepares to sleep.
The farmers make ready
seeds for sowing
when the blackthorn blooms.

But old mother Winter is not ready to rest.
I watch fine white snow
drift along the road
and I wait.

## I Thought To Send A Card | Jay Wilson

LAST WEDNESDAY I THOUGHT TO send a card, to see what's ascending on the crescent of your moon, to feel the stone you chose to push uphill, like Sisyphus. To taste those words you find absurd and cast aside in agony, before their restoration. To hear which books you recommend or helped some other one to write. I hadn't seen you in a while – you hadn't called for quite some time. I hankered to split your moon, shift its phase elsewhere, pick your brain, let you drop names, suggest we drive out with some idea at watching boats and birds off-shore, buy ice-cream cones to lick, moment by moment.

Last Wednesday I heard your afterlife caught up with you while I thought to send a card.

## Writer's Block | Ruth Taggart

I wrote a word, and the word became a sentence.
I wrote a sentence, and it gave birth to another.
I wrote a paragraph, and watched it turn into a chapter.
More chapters grew, and I had written a book.
Telling the story of you.

I try to write a book and cannot write a chapter.
I try to write a chapter, and it shrinks to a skinny paragraph.
I try to write a paragraph, and cannot form a sentence.
I cannot write a sentence as I cannot write a word.
No story to tell without you.

## Manila Envelope | Mary Cane

I'm LOOKING AT AN ENVELOPE addressed to me from my mother in Cornwall. I can't recall how many hundreds of times I've seen my address written in that hand. She has always kept up with correspondence: dating back to a strict Edwardian upbringing.

For more than fifty years I have received letters from her: since my first school trip to wherever I have lived in the world. And I have written back. The thread of care between us as strong as linen: sewing me in, keeping me safe.

This envelope's been used before, of course it has. She likes reusing paper, thread, margarine containers… rubber bands. It will have been retrieved from its storage place: the pale brown paper as soft as her skin, beside carefully wound-up string, and a bottle of gum.

No one uses manila anymore: that cheap alternative to white paper. Made from the recycled hemp rope used on sailing ships. Beaten plant fibres still showing through the paper's surface as they continue their travels.

The thing that isn't the same is the writing: my initial written too carefully as if she is leaning on my name. There's a tilt to the written lines, a hesitancy that doesn't compute with the woman who rode her motorbike from London to Cornwall to buy a dairy farm in nineteen fifty.

I remember she could quote Longfellow and Shakespeare 'til the cows came home, which they did, every morning and evening. She enjoyed all the processes of turning grass into milk. Her meticulous totting up of the amount each cow gave, was pencilled on a mucky board before she released them back to the field with a warm slap on bony rump.

There's no city name written at all. She probably hasn't jotted that down in her address book. Too obvious for those years she had a serviceable memory. Unnecessary when I've stayed in the same place for three decades.

So here it is then, just my house name and its postcode, stooping low on the envelope, taking on the loose folds of her writing arm.

## A Winter Poem | John Harvey

Now is time to consider apples.
Wind-felled or leaf-hidden
wasp-full of buzzing and decay
in tangles of late summer grass
or picked hard in the hand
and teeth-crunched open
with a bite white as snowfall.
Recall your hand too small to hold
the discovery of pips stalk and core
that intake gasp of sour.
Remember blossom too
and contemplate the naked branches
frost-still against the backyard wall.

# Green Kirtle | Roger Meachem

*I climbed Cnoc Chadail to the Knowe of Sith. There I lay hid and
watched the green kirtled folk as they sang. As the morn passed,
life flowed into the wounded wood. Tuesday March 17th. 1795.*

(FROM UNPUBLISHED WORK BY REV S. J. SWANSON)

MY SERIES ON ABERDEENSHIRE MYTHOLOGY was popular, so
when the head of a village primary school phoned me, I imagined it was to arrange a talk. No, she wanted me to write a
new article.

As I drove into her village I wondered why I hadn't visited
this place more often; *pretty* doesn't even begin to describe
it. Janet, the headteacher, had an old house on the edge of a
stunning autumnal wood and I was invited into a warm book-
lined room where her husband Richard was helping their two
young daughters with bedtime reading choices.

'Can you keep the name of the village out of it?' Janet asked
me. 'It's the woman, Aoibhe, we want you to write about. I'll
not have us become a tourist peep show.'

'The village is known already,' I answered. 'It's one of the
county's beauty spots.'

'And there's the red squirrels,' the eight-year-old piped up.

'We have beavers too.' The ten-year-old wasn't to be
outdone.

'Bedtime,' Richard told them, and to me, 'The beaver thing is still secret.'

With the children away, Richard began. 'All our memories of Aoibhe and what she did are disappearing,' he said. 'If anyone deserves credit for what's happened here, it's her, but people struggle to remember anything about her, even the colour of her hair.'

'True,' Janet jumped in, 'she stayed thirty years; left just this October, but already I can't picture her. If you don't help us, she'll be gone completely.'

'Why me?' I asked.

'You write about the Aberdeenshire Sidhe, ' Janet replied.

I could hear their eldest somewhere in the house, quietly singing an intriguing melody, but I shook my head and paid attention to her parents' tale.

In the eighties, the village had been a sad place, the woods surrounding it dying. The river was devoid of any good-sized fish, the local farm's largest field called Stone Field in honour of its only successful crop. Mice infested the houses, chewing through pipes and wires. Plumbers and electricians were frequent visitors. Then Woodview House, usually empty, was let to a new arrival, a youngish woman called Aoibhe. She was first seen putting fresh coats of paint onto Woodview's ill-fitting doors and window frames. Next, she applied herself to the bare grounds, singing as she worked. People shook their heads; no one in this village had success with gardens. "*Poor soil,*" they said.

'But she was successful,' Janet told me. 'Her garden grew ablaze with colour and alive with birds. People detoured, just to pass the house, and suddenly everyone was painting and cleaning, and the village began to shine.'

Richard spoke, 'Tell him what you always said about the singing!'

Janet paused but continued speaking about the gardens. It seemed that the local soil *was* good - if the right plants were grown - and Aoibhe was generous with her cuttings.

'It almost became a competition,' Janet told me. 'My Dad made a flower box, so our neighbours had to have one too. The Post-Office put up a hanging basket; soon, the whole of Main Street was full of flowers.'

Richard took up the story. 'Aoibhe walked everywhere. You never knew where you'd run into her, by the river, in the woods.' He looked across at his wife, 'You'd hear her singing before you saw her. A local man, Ian, had taken over the farm by then, and he was planting hedges and had free-range pigs rooting, digging up the soil. One day the press were here. He'd found the two long stones covered in Pictish symbols.'

'Richard!' Janet was cross. 'Aoibhe found the stones. Ian was about to plough the field. She got him to call people. It was the museum people came, not the press.'

I'd visited those stones, protected now from the weather by their glass structure. There were panels with explanatory notes, and nearby, Ian's organic farm shop and cafe did good business.

I asked them, 'So this woman, Aoibhe, made the Pictish find, and she had already encouraged the village to smarten up? What was it about the singing, Janet?'

'There was something exceptional about Aoibhe,' Janet began. 'It wasn't just the village; she saved our woodland. She began to plant trees, and then people joined her, planting everywhere. Ian gave up some of his land. Birds came. Even when the trees were only saplings, protected from deer by stakes, the birds came. As a child, I remember Spring mornings when the air throbbed with birdsong.'

'And Aoibhe's songs?' I persisted.

Janet took her husband's hand. 'Her songs had no words that you could recognise. But just to hear them sent shivers down your spine - shivers of happiness.'

Her daughter's song, barely audible, was doing that to me right then. I focused again and asked why the woman had left.

'One day, last October, she was simply gone,' said Richard. 'Then Woodview was put up for sale; the owners lived a long way off. But we all wanted to thank Aoibhe for so many things. The beavers! She persuaded local landowners to allow beavers - the difference they've made!'

'She was here thirty years; how old was she?'

'There's been talk about that,' Janet used a no-nonsense tone. 'She *must* have reached her fifties but looked younger. You know, one of those ageless faces.'

'No one in the village has a photo of her.' Richard seemed unaware that he was tapping my arm. 'All the things she's done and no photo. Like Macavity! That's why we called you. She mustn't be forgotten; we want you to write about her before we all forget.'

'Well,' I began, the child's song was drawing closer, 'her name is Aoibhe. Aoibhe what?'

Richard and Janet looked at me and at each other. 'We can't remember. No one can.'

'Are you telling me that no one in this village can remember the name of the woman who lived here amongst you for thirty years, whom you've known since you were children?' I grumbled. 'You remember her first name!'

'Only because we named our first child for her.'

And as if on cue, young Aoibhe came into the room carrying a drawing she must have been busy with while she was singing. It showed a woman in green surrounded by woodland creatures.

'I've drawn Tall Aoibhe,' the child said. 'Mum and Dad can't remember, but I can.'

It was a remarkable drawing for any ten-year-old to have done, but it wasn't the skill that caused the hairs on my neck to stand; it was the detail. The dress in the drawing was one I'd often seen. It was the dress worn by a woman in the frontispiece of a manuscript that I owned and had kept secret for years. I'd found the beautifully written and illustrated collection of papers at the bottom of a trunk of books I'd bought at an auction when I first moved to the county and I'd known then that the work belonged in a museum, but it had been too rich a source for me, inspiration for so many of my stories. I kept the manuscript hidden in a locked drawer, only taking it out when I felt I needed to remind myself again of the wealth of knowledge a single man had gleaned. The title was simply: *My travels in the Sithean Glens of Aberdeenshire, by Rev. Samuel. J. Swanson.*

## Walter | Brenda Conn

motherless son
of motherless son
you go to war a boy

in mud and rain
at Passchendaele
a boy you die
lie in No Man's Cot
Black Watch brothers
by your side

the sister who mothers you
a child herself
the sister who mourns you
a lifetime long
the sister who comes to you
in pilgrimage

from her

my mother learns of you
her sisters her brothers their children
their children's children
learn of you

you live in hearts you left behind
you live in hearts you never knew
ever fondly remembered

you live

## Loch Maddy High Spring
## Water Mark | Sandra Davison

Loch of the Wolf where,
in gently murmuring gloamings
or the fume of storms and waves,
blue grey shielings and lonely islands
glimpse passing ferries and searching lights.

The restless sea haunts tidelines,
surging beneath big headlands and through narrow straits,
whilst westwards the Moder Dy rises in the fog,
whispering *ciùineas ron doinnean* – homebound dangers
our ancestors would not recognise.

The North sends meltwater South, *tha am muir á lìonadh,*
overwhelming the High Spring Water Mark
as causeways, bays, piers and homes are gifted to the sea
and, with the howl of the untameable sea wolf,
coastlines return to older maps with fewer place names.


*ciùineas ron doinnean* – the calm before the storm
*tha am muir á lìonadh* – the tide is rising

## The New King | Rik Gammack

IF THERE IS A PARTICULARLY short-sighted thing to do, it is to hold a knife at a wizard's throat then demand that he help you become King. Magnus was prompted into this stupid act by a desire to right the world's wrongs and too little money to buy the spell honestly — both reasons being linked. His father had died virtually penniless, taxed into poverty by the greed of the current ruler. Magnus's older brother had inherited the farm, leaving Magnus himself with a mere ten crowns and an old plough horse. Furious at the injustice of it, Magnus had decided to take over as King and — in order to do so — to force the wizard Clotonik into helping him.

With the knife always in sight, Clotonik had fashioned a magic amulet which would make its wearer into a King. Magnus hung it round his neck with pride. 'King Magnus,' he breathed in awe.

'Huh,' grunted Clotonik, feeling his throat. 'Even magic takes time. Go to the city. You'll be King when you get there.'

It was many miles to the city, and on a narrow track through a forest, Magnus found the way blocked by a stationary wagon.

'Make way! Make way for the King!' he shouted.

A bald head popped up from the other side of the wagon and looked around. 'Where? Where's the King?'

'Here, you idiot,' Magnus snapped, tapping his chest. 'I am the King.'

'Oh?' The head didn't seem too impressed. 'You don't look like a King.'

Magnus was about to explain when he felt the amulet grow warm against his chest. He was just wondering what it meant when a look of comprehension appeared on the head, then the entire figure stepped into view and bowed low. 'I see now that you are indeed the King,' the man said. 'Please excuse my mistake, though if you'll excuse me for saying so, it was an easy one to make. You are not — if you'll pardon me, Sire — dressed as befits your station.'

Magnus looked down at his rough farm clothes. The ragged bits that held the holes together were shapeless and dirty. 'You're right,' he sighed. 'What shall I do?'

'Well, Sire, I am a travelling tailor,' the man said, gesturing towards his wagon. 'For five crowns I could make you a new suit of clothes fit for your station.'

Half his inheritance! It would be worth it though. 'Agreed,' Magnus said.

The tailor worked swiftly and completed the suit by the following dawn. Magnus was delighted with his new appearance and, even though he suspected that the gold buttons were really polished brass, he thanked his destiny for bringing the tailor to him.

Later that day, Magnus's horse cast a shoe and began to limp. However, there was a village just over the next hill and Magnus led the beast there to be shod.

When he arrived at the forge, he found the smith asleep on a pile of sacking. 'Wake up, wake up,' Magnus cried. 'The King's horse needs shoeing.'

The bleary-faced smith shot to his feet and looked around wildly. 'The King? Where? I don't see him.'

'Here, you fool,' declared Magnus. 'I'm the King.'

The smith frowned darkly and seemed about to say something when again Magnus felt the amulet grow warm. As it did so, the smith's eyes widened and he sank to one knee. 'Your Majesty, please forgive me for not recognising you. If you'll excuse me for saying so, it was your horse that fooled me. I would have expected you to be riding a finer beast than that.'

Magnus had to agree with him. The old plough horse was a tired, sway-backed beast well past its prime. 'You're right,' Magnus said. 'What should I do?'

'Well, Sire, it happens I've got a fine white charger in the stable. You can have it and its tack, which is studded with silver, for five crowns. I'll even take your own poor creature off your hands.'

Magnus agreed, and though he suspected that his new mount was white through age, and that the cracked leather was studded with tin instead of silver, the last of his inheritance seemed a small price to pay for creating a good impression.

So it was that a penniless but proud Magnus finally arrived at the closed gates of the city. 'Open up,' he called. 'Open up for the King.'

A dishevelled guard sauntered out of the watch house to confront him.

'And who are ...' The guard's voice trailed off as once more the amulet pulsed with heat. 'The King,' he declared in amazement. 'You're the King.'

'I am,' declared Magnus, full of pride. 'I'm King Magnus, the new ruler of this land.' The guard laughed roughly, then yelled out, 'Hey, lads. The King's here. The King's back.' Several more men tumbled from the watch house. Most were peasants, armed with pitchforks and scythes. They took one look at Magnus then called to others within the city. In minutes Magnus was surrounded by a grinning crowd, and as the amulet glowed hot enough to scorch his skin they cried, 'It's the King. The King's returned.'

But the pride within Magnus's chest curdled into something sour at the expression on their faces.

'Well, actually ...' he began, as rough hands pulled him from his mount. '... I'm not ...' he continued, but the words were cut off by a rope jerked tight around his neck. '... Not really ...' he croaked, as the rope was flung over a low branch. '... The King,' he finished, too late for anyone to hear.

The peasants had already solved the problem of cruel laws and onerous taxes, and Clotonik's amulet flared brightly as the new King swung gently in the breeze.

# Their Sound in Lockdown | Leela Gautam

Every day, twice a day, he stands there,
separated from her, glass between them.
A space so small he would touch her,
hug her, if only he could.

Her gnarled fingers trace crooked lines
over steaming breath.
Rheumy eyes crinkle through unshed tears.
Lips quiver in deep, unspoken pain.

He waves the hand without the stick as
she lifts the hand the nurse holds.
Air kisses fly, bounce back and land.
Tears drip into the mouth that calls her name.

It's her heart that hears his voice,
her ears cannot. She whispers his name.
Each day they wait for this,
their sound in lockdown.

## Night Voyaging | Mary Cane

Our beds are ships that carry us through seas of the night,
with counterpane sails and eiderdown rope,
billowing linen, stitched, bewitched
in the navy moonlight.

Sailing rudderless through our warm, shadowed dreams,
star-gazey, stir-crazy, unshackled from care,
emboldened, enfolded we tack and gibe,
leaning, two sheets to the winds.

In the morning we disembark, like larks,
to enter the fray of the day,
the bed left beached, bleached, safe anchorage,
awaiting remaking, for the next voyage.

## The Face of an Angel | Ann Nicol

MARY HARRISON'S GAZE WANDERED FOR a moment around
the classroom that had been her domain for so many years,
taking in the brightly coloured pictures and the lop-sided
models on the windowsill. Her job had been a very demand-
ing one and finally she had been forced to admit that she no
longer had the energy to do it properly. Until recently 'early
voluntary retirement' had been a phrase bandied around by
others. She smiled wryly to herself – Mary Harrison, M.A.,
E.V.R. It sounded rather grand.

Her class would be coming to say their goodbyes in five
minutes or so and she must be ready. A luncheon had been
held in her honour earlier in the day and thankfully the goodbyes of the staff were behind her.

Only one more chore to do. She began to empty her desk.
One or two exercise books were joined in the waste-paper
basket by three caramels, squashed and sticky in their wrap-
pers, an ancient 'Beano', a hideous black rubber spider and a
wizened conker still strung for action. Finally she rapped the
upturned drawers smartly to clear out the corners and replaced
them. The right-hand one proved awkward to the last. She sat
down and ran her hands slowly, with affection almost, over the
old wooden desk. In the bottom left-hand corner the surface

was uneven, and Mary Harrison did not need to see the cause. 'M.H. loves W.N.' had been carved, or, more accurately, gouged out of the woodwork. She remembered the day well – Stephen Brown, full of pretended innocence, had paid dearly in extra homework for that particular piece of vandalism.

The message had been true, but 'W.N.' died with many others in the Allies' escape from Dunkirk and that had been that. She had just begun her teaching career. As if to chase away the memory, Mary wiped her hands briskly with her handkerchief and took a mirror from her handbag to check on the upswept greying hair, the trim lace collar. Yes, she was quite presentable.

Soon the children arrived, looking in her direction and giggling nervously as they made their way with clattering feet to their seats. As usual, it was Jenny who managed to make more noise than anyone. Mary looked at the child's untidy red hair and sullen mouth, at the wrinkled socks and trailing shoelaces. She wondered why it was this girl, more than any of the others, that she would miss. The child became aware of her gaze and looked at her rebelliously.

When Jenny had first come to the school, Mary had despaired of teaching her anything. She was convinced Jenny had neither interest nor inclination to study until she discovered the girl's talent for drawing – people mostly, but animals, too, came to life under her inspired pencil. Mary fostered that talent even in opposition to Jenny's mother, who wanted her daughter to stop 'this silly scribbling' as she called it and do something useful.

When the noise subsided Mary came from behind her desk and stood facing the class. She smiled at them and, when finally all were quiet, said clearly, 'As you know, this is my last day at school, and tomorrow your new teacher will be here. Although I am saying goodbye to you, I want you to know that if you have any problems, you can come and see me and talk to me at any time.' In spite of herself her eyes strayed to Jenny's face but it remained closed and expressionless.

Mary spoke for a little longer and finally said that they must be anxious to be gone and she would say no more, but hoped that they would help the new teacher. She returned to her desk and the children came forward and, one by one, left a small gift in front of her. She was surprised and touched as she knew they had very little in the way of pocket-money. The only one who did not come was Jenny and Mary did not even see her leave the room. She put her coat on, and stowed her gifts in pockets and handbag. She felt unaccountably depressed. So many years of her life dedicated to her charges. Had it been worth it? Just at that moment, she thought not.

It was raining as she made her way to her car and the windscreen was blurred. She was watching the wipers clearing the field of vision when there was a tap at the window. It was Jenny, coatless and wet in the cold October wind. Mary wound down the window. 'Jenny, you must put on your coat on,' she began but Jenny thrust an envelope into her hand and rushed away, to stand watching from the shelter of the school door. Mary wound up the window as the rain was now quite heavy. The envelope was grubby. Mary took from it a single sheet of paper. The face drawn there was undoubtedly hers and her feeling of depression deepened. Was this really how the child saw her? The frowning face, pulled-back hair, eyes like laser beams and grim turned-down mouth? Jenny had scored two dark lines through the drawing and when Mary looked closer, she saw that 'turn over' was written at the bottom of the page.

The tears that had been lurking all day spilled over. The other drawing was exquisite in its use of light and shade. Before her was her own face, beautiful as it had never been - the face of an angel, the expression soft and the eyes full of compassion. Scarcely able to see through her tears, Mary Harrison opened the window again and blew the watching child a kiss. There was no response and after a minute Mary slipped the car into gear. In her mirror she could see Jenny still standing at the school door and saw, too, Jenny's fingers go up to her lips and return the gesture.

Mary drove on, past the sign that that she had passed so many times before – *Beechgreen School for the Profoundly Deaf* – and turned out onto the highway.

## Just as Her Soul Departed | Ian Taggart

If you could see, as I have seen,
last gasps where life had been,
pale sallow skin to set the scene,
just as her soul departed.

If you could hear, as I have heard,
the rasping breath that all have heard,
the heaving chest that takes no air,
just as her soul departed.

If you could feel, as I have felt,
the ice cold hand of death I felt,
alone but not alone, I was here
just as her soul departed.

If you could cry, as I have cried,
to lose this soul, I cried,
no time to dwell, for there is more –
just another soul departed.

## DIY Regrets | Richard Anderson

I gave it the once-over, twice,
then against accepted advice,
I jammed the thing in a vice
and twisted it sharply.
At the time, I viewed this with spice,
but, in retrospect, darkly.

I surveyed the wreckage and thought
of the hurt and damage I'd wrought
by failing to properly plot
before taking action,
the fine preparation that ought
to precede satisfaction.

I absorbed disappointment and then,
resisting the urge to abstain,
resolved to deal with the strain
of trying again.
*I'll change my approach!* I exclaimed,
just not quite sure when.

## Wee Meg | Andy Fairnie

SHE TRAIPSES IN AND DROPS hersel doon across the other side o the fire fi me. Claws at thon adder bite she got when she wis a bairn. Done wi that, she keeks through the fire at me, the flames flittin ower her shadowy face. Eye'n me wi the black een through thon daft fringe o hers. The 'Scabbard Makers Dauchter', the fair heedit yin, last o ma three. Richt then a shiver came ower me, I kent whit was comin. She screwed her face up at the reek.

'Faither it's ma time is come noo as weel'.

'I knew it,' I said to masel, no speakin. I mind seein thon look aboot her when he had come tae deal wi me ower the new scabbard.

I watched her mother turnin in her bed to face the clay waa. I couldnae mak oot through the reek if her back was still, or if it was shooglin wi silent greetin.

'Him that deelt the new scabbard isn't it?' as if I didnae ken. 'Another sodjer?'

'Aye, he's a Centurion!' As bold as brass is she no?

'But ye cannie even speak thur tongue!' She draws up her knees and keeks at me fi ahint thum.

'He's learnin me; amo, amas, amat...' she sniggers. I feel like liftin ma hand ti her. But I jist stare at the new scabbard I'm polishin wi-oot seein it. The last coat o sap has torket in, and it'll syne be done. It looked richt worthy earlier ootside in the daylicht.

'How can nane o yis find a man among oor ain?'

Mars | Lucy Anderson

WHEN ALANA MET MARS ON the steps of the church, she asked him one question: *Like the planet or like the god?* Mars didn't know.

Years later, as they stood at the shadowy altar, Alana thought she'd made up her mind. Mars' fingers curled around the grip of his gun too easily; the blood stained his face like a blush, giving him a twisted, inhuman sort of beauty. War had changed Alana. It suited Mars. How could someone who slipped so easily into conflict be named after a piece of rock?

Alana's knees hit stone, her hands dropping to her sides as she knelt before Mars. Her gun lay empty on the ground, discarded at the end of an abandoned pew. The picnics and movie nights had always been leading them back to the church, but instead of white, Alana wore the blue of sirens and flashing lights. As always, Mars wore red.

The loaded barrel aimed at her heart, the clouds of her breath in the dusty air, the way Mars looked at her as if they'd never been anything but enemies; Alana took it all in, and she accepted it. Whatever happened at that altar, however they'd come to be there and whatever wrongs they'd both done in the war, Alana was glad it was Mars. It was always Mars.

There, in the shadow of stone angels, Alana said her final

prayer. But as the bullet shattered her heart and she looked up at Mars, with his bright red hair and even brighter uniform, she changed her mind. There were no gods in that church. The saints in the windows only watched as she fell, daring her to ask for salvation.

It had always been the planet. Red hair, red rock. It was that simple. There were no gods in war, not even Mars.

# Kintsugi | Hema Kamath

Smooth, fluid, molten gold,
filling the cracks
of stories untold.

It tells a story: the creases
made safe and bright. Always
perfect, always right. Making
them new, precious too.

It's a scrap but it's pretty,
from something
I made for your daddy.

I piece my quilt, fill the gaps:
a snip of this, a strip of that,
flashes of special times, gone fast,

to joyfully sew anew
stories and adventures, too,
down generations, just for you.

*Kintsugi or 'golden joinery' is the Japanese art of illuminating
and strengthening with precious metals items that have been
damaged. It comes from a philosophy of 'no waste'.*

# The Office Runs Itself | Mark Pithie

SINCE THE LOCKDOWN STARTED, *what was it, four, maybe five weeks ago,* Alan had lost all track of time. Each day seemed to merge into the next. Like all of the working population, he had always looked forward to Friday, the start of the weekend, when people went on nights out to pubs and clubs, met friends for coffee, that sort of thing, in what seemed like another life, another time that had receded into history.

He now looked forward to his daily Exercise Time of 3.30pm, and today it was even bright and sunny – a bonus in late April in the North-East of Scotland. This was when he escaped his flat and walked as far as he could in an hour. It was an absolute delight to be out in the open, in the fresh air, and to gaze up at the wide expanse of pale blue sky. It really made him feel glad to be alive, to appreciate things that he had previously taken for granted, like bird song, the smells of flowers, the heat of the sun's rays.

This, he thought, was also a great chance to reignite memories, to mull over ideas for stories, poems, and articles which he would publish on his website, now more popular since Lockdown had started. An amateur writer, he had been writing daily since being furloughed from his job, with no real end to this on the horizon. He was working on a novella, a piece of autobiographical fiction describing his life in the 1980s, he had written 8900 words. It was going well, just a question of getting it right and editing out the stuff he did not need, separating the wheat from the chaff.

His next project was to be a supernatural horror story. He had done something like this successfully a few years before but wondered if those who visited his website would want anything of this nature now, given that this Virus really embodied the ultimate horror. Which raised the question, where did a writer of this genre go now, did they return to the ghost story style of the late 19th century, ghost stories of antiquity, like M.R. James, or to the weird and elemental, 'folk horror' style of Arthur Machen and Algernon Blackwood? Alan was not at all sure but was willing to give either option a try, after all he had the time, bags of it, on his hands. He preferred the understated, eerie stories of Ramsey Campbell and Thomas Ligotti to authors who dealt in vivid description of gratuitous bloodletting and gushing gore. On his afternoon walk, he would let his mind wander and ideas would come to him, rushing headlong like idiots flouting social distancing laws.

Every day for the last two weeks, he had walked past the empty office blocks of the oil industry which had once made Aberdeen a proud city, the oil capital of Europe, back in the halcyon days of the 80s. These vacant husks of concrete, steel and glass now lay empty, serving as mausoleums of an industry in decline. There were no vehicles in the car park, only a congregation of corvids holding court in their place. He walked towards the office blocks and could see that one of the fire escapes was open. *What the hell*, there were not going to be any security staff in the place, he would go in and have a look around. He was not a housebreaker, simply curious, as a child might be. What could possibly happen?

What struck him first was the eerie silence in the place, and how cold it was. How old was this building, maybe late 1960s? It was not just ancient buildings that could be haunted. Maybe this could be his story idea. He was surprised at how light it was inside the building, so many windows. A smell of disinfectant permeated the area, as it had Alan's own workplace. The cleaning staff must have been working overtime, effectively all the time, to sanitize the buildings once the onset of the Virus had been confirmed. He walked along a corridor festooned with Coronavirus safety notices. The carpet was gaudily patterned and threw images in his mind from some old horror movie. He opened a door with a start as it squealed in protest after weeks of disuse. He continued up a flight of stairs, the bannisters and stone steps reminding him of school back in the 70s, his footsteps echoing in the void of the stairwell.

Opening another creaking door, he stepped into the office, an open-plan suite, which looked like the staff had left in a hurry, as if the fire alarm had gone off. One of the computers was still on, pens and pencils and other office stationery lying about, as if their owners would be returning soon. There was a rustling from behind him, *just the wind*, he said to himself. Sure enough, someone had left a window open and the blinds were blowing slightly. There was nobody in here, *was there?* He checked the corridor. At the far end he could have sworn that the door moved, as if someone had gone through it, or opened it to see who was in the building. Maybe there was a security guard?

He walked back into the office. Looking at the paraphernalia on the desks, he spotted a book by Edgar Allan Poe, opened at 'The Masque of the Red Death'. *Wasn't that a story about a contagion?* It was accompanied by a couple of others, 'Lost Girl' by Adam Nevill, and 'The Journal of the Plague Year' by Daniel Defoe. Someone in this place had been reading about contagions. He wondered momentarily about the owner of these books, but he, or she, was not around. Would he swipe them for himself? He liked horror, so Poe and Nevill would be great, Defoe he would definitely keep, *what the hell*. He fumbled them into the side pockets of his jacket and heard the rustling sound behind him again.

'*Hello?*' he said to the silence.

He left the office and walked back along the corridor – the door was moving again, making a swishing sound. He ran to the door and opened it, no evidence of anyone there.

'*Hello?*'

The silence offered no response. He was imagining things. He had been on his own too long during Lockdown. Living on your own was a good thing most of the time but sometimes it made you doubt yourself, imagine and escalate things in your mind. He would have another look in the office, what harm would it do?

He returned to the desk where the computer was still on. He tapped the keyboard and clicked the mouse. *Bloody hell!* There was a story about contagions, plagues and things on the computer. The person with all the books must be a fellow writer.

*Wow, here was a coincidence*, the character in the story was called Alan, and he had just entered an empty office in a city during Lockdown. Hearing the sound again, he looked around, there was someone in the room with him, wasn't there? Maybe it was just a security guard coming to eject him from the building, maybe, just maybe.

# The Blackthorn Winter | Tina Haddon

The Blackthorn, legendary, magical,
tree or hedge, can live a hundred years.
Home for fairies, witches, wildlife,
shared. From dense tangled branches,
nightingales sing, purple sloes to flavour
our gin, bark - a medicinal pledge.

Only the foolish ignore the legends, and dare
the wrath of the Cailleach.

The sap moon has risen, snowdrops
have passed, primroses smile from
the ground, blackthorn is flowering:
every twig, every spike, white lace petals,
bird song resounds, sun's warmth, beguiling.

Crows busy with urgent repairs, thieve
twigs from neighbours, arguments abound,
new life emerging. Spring stretches and yawns.

Winter returns, a last gasp, refusing to be
banished by Spring. Birds stop singing, green
tips stalted, unfurling leaves halted, nothing
spared this Arctic blast. Swirling snow showers,
pelting hail force April lambs indoors. For some,
they will perish, too cold to be nourished.

Who has done what to the Blackthorn tree?
Ignoring the legends and dared
the wrath of the Cailleach?

# The Man Who Walked Backwards | Alistair MacRaild

EVERY EVENING AROUND SEVEN O'CLOCK Robyn felt he was actually going to burst into tears. All of a sudden this success- ful and respected accountant felt his eyes welling up.

It was precisely an hour until his next medication. When an impassive, some would say altogether unlovely, nurse called Coraline, would give him his pills. Pills he liked to think were white pebbles. How Hansel (Gretel's brother) had used them, and applied to Robyn's situation, appealed to him.

'But, I digress,' he said. He was straddling a chair. The back of his head faced me. 'Listen. A year ago (a year after the flood it feels like) I had a dream. I was an ant pulling food the long way back to the hill... When I woke there was a sense, no more than a sense, of restraint. Though it seemed I couldn't shift my arms to a particular position, nor for that matter move my legs a certain way, it didn't strike me as strange, still being half asleep. It was only when I tried to get out of bed that I began to think something was wrong. There was no pain. No physical pain. Just, how can I say, a general feeling of an inability to move the way I wanted to. After a bit of pushing and grabbing, some at contemplation, I managed to get out of bed, but it was only achieved as if I were stepping off a ladder, or out of the carriage of an old steam train, which had been, I imagined, heading West.

'At this juncture, my new problem shifted into flat-light. Other priorities came into sharp focus. I had to wash and dress. I had an office to attend, and punctually. I loved my job.

'But it just wouldn't go. As I moved 'towards' the bathroom it became abundantly and shockingly clear, I had begun to walk backwards. Physically, it had quickly become normal, just as if I was walking forwards. Mentally, as you can see before you, it was to become another thing.'

## An Old Road | Peter Noble

The old roads were not so wide.
They were created out of the countryside.
The days of tobacco and wine. Nostalgic time.

We were living in the surge
of purge after purge.

We had the trade, and cotton lines.
Industry was setting out
to mechanise and improve.
The factory men and women
were tested to the limit.

The great houses were visited
by foreign dignitaries.
The circus was fully lived.
British standards were forged
out of iron and steel hope.

Belief in the glory,
determination to share its story.
We were fabulous at construction.
We had steam and piston.
Brilliant fashion was never far away.

The crows fly past and remember old trends.

Very cruel to have to mend
the disappointments.
The verges are cut
by the side of an old road.

## Doric Anthem for Doomed England | Ian Anderson

Fit passin-bells fir them fa vote lik cattle,
Deein fit the tabloid papers say?
Fa jine the high-class racist's rabid rabble
Tae sneer at fowk fa'r forrin, Scots or gay?
Jist mockeries fir them fir laas an deals,
Nor ony soond o mournin save the choirs,
The blin, dementit choirs o swickit feels,
Fa folla yon Pied Piper fae sad shires.

Nae cannel sall be lit tae ca them hame,
Lik yon fit burns fir Scotland in the fauld
O freens fa wilnae leave us in the cauld.
Nae warmth sall win intae their herts o stane;
Their epitaph the void o peer, teem minds,
An fan hope fades, the draain-doon o blinds.

Kiev 1920 | Andy Fairnie

AT THAT TIME, WE LIVED together in a lace and mahogany furnished apartment, up a flight of creaking stairs in a stale tenement block near St. Sophia's. My wife Viktoriya had her own small shop where she worked every day, a haberdashery and milliners. You might say it was dingy, as little natural light got past the high block opposite, which excluded all but the boldest shafts of sunlight. A pair of heavy oil lamps hanging on chains strove to keep the pressing shadows at bay. The shop was built into our magnolia-faced building at street level, behind two windows and its own glass and wood door, complete with a tinkling bell. Near the door stood a tall narrow glass cabinet displaying the finest eye-catching ladies' hats. There were cabinets filled with trays of coloured cotton reels. Some of the counter tops had worn brass rules screwed into the edges to measure cloth, which was stored in loose bolts on dark shelves around the panelled walls. Though of diminutive height, Viktoriya did not mind demonstrating the strength of her lithe little body, eagerly lifting and wielding those sizeable cloth bolts at every opportunity. The wood was dark and well-worn maybe, but solid and ancient. Once every year the landlady would turn up and coat it in a thick dark varnish.

Viktoriya was constantly busy in the shop. She was industrious, inviting and always smiling; a knowing, perhaps cheeky, smile, with a glint in her eye. Wearing her hair up, as she always did in daytime, gave her a prim look, unless of course a wayward lock came loose, as she hurried around her shop, dispatching happy customers and welcoming new. Sometimes, when the shop was empty, she would stand alone in a solitary shaft of sunlight, silver-lit dust floating around her luminous form. Behind closed eyes she would dance a childhood dance around the bare wooden corners of her father's craning outbuildings.

At night, home in our lamp-lit rooms, she would lift off her hair band and shrug loose her thick, dark hair. Then she would look up at me, eyes sparkling, and give me a teasing 'catch me if you can' look. Our smiles would hold for a few seconds before cracking into laughter, and I would chase her, giggling, across the herringbone parquet and around the two chairs and table, until she would spin around and pull herself up, hands on hips and proffering her best matronly frown. Then, as our shadows came together across the faded wallpaper, we would sigh contentedly, and embrace. The day's trials and tomorrow's foreboding would lift and gently drift away, leaving us cleansed, mellow and deep in our untarnished love.

## When I Arrived | Lou Parra

When I arrived, it took me by surprise:
someone had come into my studio
to calmly move my belongings.

The fact almost resembled a game,
there was an eerie stillness.

Sharp-eyed, noticing a movement
to my left, just two and a half inches
turn to the south. I had the sensation
that this was a previously hidden place,
with my totems afloat and in limbo.

The objects, weighing a lot,
  C- O-
      L- L- A- P-
          S- E- D.

A dead father returned.
He must be very desolate.

I grieve for the circumstances,
but we search for knowledge
to place our souls and feet
in a less patriarchal world
more to the south,
more to the left
and selfless.

## The Woman's Self | Ruth Taggart

The woman's Self came and sat beside her,
quite unexpectedly,
one day of sun, and grass.

*Who are you?* asked the woman.
It had been so long since their last meeting
that she did not recognise her Self.

*I am the part of you,* said Self,
*that you left behind. Don't you remember?*
*The part who longs for romance, and beauty, and God.*

*The part who takes lovers*
*and risks. And who travels to far-off beaches*
*or dances on pavements at night,*

*and who looks at the sky, its scale and scope,*
*and decides to breathe the whole in,*
*and has that breath taken back by the wind, and laughs.*

*Don't you remember? I'll show you.*
*Come now, with me, far away from here.*
*You will see that I am your Self.*

But the woman's favourite telly show was about to start
and she had a pork chop defrosting for tea.
So she said to her Self *it was nice to meet you,*
*but I'd better get on.*

## Altered Images | Dominique Anderson

THIS MORNING FOUND JULIA FLUTTERING between slumber and wakefulness. The previous night, she'd had one of the many quarrels that were occurring more and more frequently with her daughter. Sophie was in the habit of criticising her mother a lot. It wasn't significant now, but it had bothered Julia. She always took those 'words' to heart, which probably resulted in Sophie's fire being further fuelled. Others didn't take them so seriously and Julia started to keep quiet about their importance, and to keep quiet about most subjects, rarely displaying any genuine feelings at all. After their argument, Julia had decided on impulse to go out for a drive to relieve her stress, despite the torrential rain.

The two women sported the same vibrant red hair but, as Sophie loved to consider, couldn't be more different. Sophie did her best to highlight any differences. This initially took the form of golden streaks and daily attempts at straightening the thick curly hair that was a family hallmark. Later, it became the systematic criticism of almost anything Julia uttered.

Sophie had moved out of the house five years previously,

yet her mother still clung to the items that her daughter had accumulated in the somewhat cramped, yet comfortable, bedroom she had lovingly created for her. Julia should really have given some away, at least the things that Sophie could not take, or didn't want any more.

The large Edwardian doll's house that took pride of place was a good example. It had always been a permanent feature in the bedroom and Sophie had spent many hours playing with the tiny figurines as a child, and even as a young teenager, although she hated to admit that. The house featured three bedrooms, a sitting room and even a billiard room with a pink chintz sofa and curtains to match. It had many charming details – pine furniture, pictures on walls, even enchanting blue willow pattern cups and saucers. Three contemporary inhabitants in modern outfits replaced the original, long lost figurines. Somehow, Julia had never been able to part with that doll's house.

This morning, as she slowly opened her mind, and then her eyes, to the day ahead, it appeared earlier than she had previously thought. The room seemed bathed in an unreal darkness and Julia found the lack of light eerie, although she wasn't sure what made her reach that conclusion. A few minutes passed. Then, suddenly, she sat up, startled by the realisation...

Although they looked familiar, the curtains were not her own! The shock and confusion of the situation soon gave way to acceptance. She remembered seeing those curtains every day – from outside. She knew before opening the next door what she would find there. The billiard table had looked out of place before. It didn't today, nor did the flowery sofa and curtains. It wasn't where she normally lived. But it had the colour of home.

Somewhere on the other side of town, a young woman stepped into the bright, white casualty ward and stared at the isolated bed as she approached the still, familiar figure.

# A Pedant's Demise | Richard Anderson

A sedentary pedant
sat a-pedanting one day,
when a misplaced comma
tinkered with his mind.

Punctuation predilection
caused his brain to fry with friction
as a hypertensive hyphen
sabotaged his day.

His digestive tract was twisted
by a random semi colon
and a less or fewer conflict
caused blood pressure to rise.

His arteries were hardened
as infinitives were split
and at a much in place of many
his heartbeat simply ceased.

A polished granite headstone
with letters neatly carved
proclaims for all posterity:
'Here rest's a pre-cise man'.

## Encounter | Martin Walsh

EARLY MARCH, ABERDEEN. A HAAR hovers low over the city sucking all colour out of the landscape. An air of gloom stalks the empty backstreets.

But Tim, the artist newly arrived from Ironbark, Australia, seems oblivious, enchanted even: note the brightness of his eyes, the tranquillity of his demeanour. The greys do not seem to touch *him*, he walks serene beneath his wide black beret topped by its little exclamation mark. Perhaps the contrasts are what animate him: the cool whiff of ocean after the parched scent of outback, the keening of gulls exchanged for the shrieks of cockatoos, the solidity of granite and slate swapped for the flimsiness of clapboard and corrugated iron.

He daunders homewards along empty backwynds, a small wiry figure – all in black but for an aubergine scarf wound, Aristide Bruant-style, around his collar. His paintings hung and with two clear days before the exhibition, he emanates contentment. He stoops, attracted by a tiny fern growing out of a wall, peering over his specs, to touch it. The fern is luminous, almost emerald against the sun-dark skin of his hands; on its leaves droplets of dew glow in the dull light. Captivated, he forgets time until a sudden gust of wind ruffles the tangle of dark curls un-ensnared by his beret.

He sets off and quickens pace under a sky threatening rain, his elegant, black walking boots silent on the cobbles. On the road ahead, his attention is caught by a figure looming out of the mist. There is something odd about it, something vaguely unsettling. It veers towards him.

As the apparition approaches, the details sharpen. It's a man. Not a huge man, but the spiky, ginger Mohican hairstyle lends it a certain height and menace. The skin has an un-earthly pallor and there are studs in the nose and lips. Beneath a worn leather waistcoat, a red tartan shirt hangs loose over camouflage breeks; below these are scuffed bovver boots, their steel toecaps scraping the cobbles. The figure stops, blocking the artist's path, fixing Tim in his gimlet gaze.

'Fit like?' The voice is gruff, strongly accented, belligerent even. *Is this a question or a threat?* Tim looks for possible escape routes, other passers-by. There are none.

'G'day?'

'Aa've got somethin for ye!'

'Yeah?'

'Come 'ere then, ah'm nae gaun tae bite ye.' They approach one another, the ghost-faced Mohican and the little tanned Aussie:

'Ah'm gaun tae gie ye a hug. Is that a'richt wi you?'

'OK by me.' The voice uncertain.

The Mohican grasps him in a bear hug accompanied by the rank aroma of one who sleeps rough. The embrace is brief, heartfelt, non-threatening – an unexpected collision of two worlds.

'There. That wisna sae bad, wis it?'

'No, it was... it was... good. Would you like one back?'

'Aye.'

This time it is Tim who initiates the hug. No further words are exchanged but a strange sense of well-being envelops him. All the way home, oblivious to the rain now dripping off his beret and the curious glances of passers-by, Tim's face is transfixed by a grin.

Back in Australia, in the old converted bakery which is his studio, the memory of that encounter sometimes revisits him and he wonders about the Mohican. One day he steps out of his studio to give his wife, Lynn, an unexpected hug as she hangs up the laundry. She looks at him quizzically then laughs: 'What's that for?' But he just smiles and breathes in the sweetness of her perfume.

## An Old Poet's Complaint | John Harvey

I recall how days in my youth
were easy, long and a half truth
could cue a song. Not now, for now

though days rush by, the mind winds slow,
needing more time than years ago
to forge a rhyme, or justify

a tendered draft of clumsy verse.
I must admit it's now more curse
than benefit, this cruel craft.

It taunts with themes beyond my skill,
while words evade my grasp – yet still,
work can be made from damaged dreams.

And to what end? What's left for me
that might inspire new poetry
but the desire to please a friend?

## Teallach | Sandra Davison

I wish the Peace of the Glen for you
and the whisper of the breeze for you;
I wish the Warmth of the Sun for you
and the Song of the Dawn for you.

When we meet again – and I hope we may –
may we walk in companionable silence
before sitting by the dancing flames
beneath the flowing light of the *Na Fir-chlis*.

And when the owls call down the Glen
may we coorie in, and with a wee bosie
allow our gentle words to settle like embers
glowing against the gathering darkness?

*Teallach* – Scottish Gaelic for hearth
*Na Fir-chlis* – Scottish Gaelic for the Northern Lights

# Biographies

### Dominique Anderson
Dominique Anderson writes short stories and poems. She also paints, sometimes to illustrate her writing. She finds her pets to be a never-ending source of inspiration.

### Ian Anderson
Ian Anderson writes poetry in both English and Doric, and the occasional short story. He is inspired by his wife and fellow writer Dominique and by their pets.

### Lucy Anderson
Student and lifelong fantasy enthusiast. Lover of all things history, folklore and fairytale; inspired by nothing more than cultures of the past, especially those of Scottish and Norse heritage.

### Richard Anderson
After retiring as a Chartered Surveyor he was surprised to find that he could write a type of poetry. He tries to make a serious point in a light-hearted manner.

### Mary Cane
I enjoy writing about archaic and nostalgic family topics. They support my ethnological research on the contemporary grandmother experience, and the optimistic notion that future family will be eternally grateful.

### Brenda Conn
Brenda writes poetry and short stories mainly in English, occasionally in Doric. A long-abandoned novel gathers dust but may yet be resurrected and inflicted upon fellow Lemon Tree Writers.

### Sandra Davison

Retired from paid work, result pending from University of Aberdeen MLitt in Creative Writing, embarking on MGAlba's forthcoming SpeakGaelic course, intrigued by dwelling in the places of our cultural heritage.

### Andy Fairnie

Raised in fishing, matured in oil. Lived twenty years abroad raising a Norwegian family. Grandfather.

### Rik Gammack

Retirement is a second childhood where I can make up stories about invented people and places, then illustrate them. Am I allowed to have this much fun?

### Leela Gautam

A retired doctor, Leela has written poetry since schooldays in India with several publications. Her poems have appeared in showcases by Poetryspace.co.uk and in their Lockdown anthology.

### Tina Haddon

Nature, macro and the micro, is my first love. Writing my second – like a permanent itch ignored at my peril. The included poem encapsulates both passions.

### John Harvey

John has worked as chicken plucker, private tutor, mural painter, schoolmaster, builder's labourer, theatre director, council gardener, dramatist and lemonade delivery man. He lives in Meigle.

### Hema Kamath

Hema writes poems just for the sheer pleasure of expressing her thoughts. Not having written for four decades, the Covid situation has awakened her urge to write again.

### Alasdair MacRaild

Alastair lives in Aberdeen and likes films and cooking.

### Roger Meachem

Roger tells tales. He writes for fun when he isn't gazing at the stars, walking along a beach or dreaming of strange worlds.

### Ann Nicol

Ann Nicol has been writing short stories and articles for many years, mostly in the doric and has been greatly assisted by the Lemon Tree Writers Group in Aberdeen.

### Peter Noble

Peter is an enthusiast of modern poetry. His education in Aberdeen has helped shape his literary themes. He enjoys poetry about national history. Old songs and poems inspire.

### Lou Parra

Lou Parra is a Mexican author living in Scotland. She teaches at the University of Aberdeen. The poem 'When I arrived' is part of her Spanglish play 'Deep pool'.

### Mark Pithie

Mark Pithie is a writer from Aberdeen. He has turned his hand to prose in recent years, contributing regularly to various websites. His work is posted on ABCTales.com.

## Ian Taggart

Ian is a new member of the group and an alumnus of the University of Aberdeen. He is best described as a general writer focusing on short stories and poetry.

## Ruth Taggart

Ruth writes occasional poems and procrastinates over writing a novel. Mostly, though, she just hangs around the LTW in the hope that the group will be a positive influence.

## Sarah-Jane Toleman

I am inspired by the natural world from landscapes to leaves. I am the mother of two grown-up girls, a teacher and the guardian of a black cat.

## Martin Walsh

Retired Marine Biologist, turned writer. Long-term devotee of LTW – now the group's first official dinosaur. Favourite themes: Africa, Latin America, magical realism, absurdist military memoir.

## Jay Wilson

Banff-based dog walker, Jay Wilson, is an emerging writer whose poem *Noah's Daughter* was long-listed for the Fish Poetry Award, and contributed a non-fiction feature to *Scotland's Secret History*.